ELIYAS EXPLAINS

Angels

MUSLIM CHILDREN'S BOOKS

Published by Muslim Children's Books 2020

ISBN 978-1-9160236-5-9

 British Library Cataloguing in Publication Data. A catalogue record for this book is available from the British Library.

muslimchildrensbooks.co.uk

Muslim
Children's
Books

Zanib Mian
illustrated by Daniel Hills

ELIYAS EXPLAINS

Muslim Children's Books

ASALAMU ALAIKUM

(Did you know that means, 'Peace be with you.' So Salaam is basically greetings of peace).

Anyway, I am **Eliyas**, and this is what I see when I look in the mirror.

You don't know me, but you will, slowly.

Here are some things I can tell you in advance:

FACTS ABOUT ME:

fact 1. I have one little brother,

3 years old and very sticky

and one little sister.

6 years old and very sneaky.

Aasiya

I have just drawn their heads, but obviously they have bodies too.

fact 2.

I like animals. I mean I **LOVE** them. I will go and hold any animal I see on the road, except like donkeys and horses, because they are obviously too **big** to hold, and they're not normally on the road anyway, unless you're in Pakistan or Morocco or something.

fact 3.

Because of the above, once, a chicken pooped in my lap. ON MY FAVOURITE JEANS.

PS the chicken was on the road, strangely enough. But that's another story...

fact 4.

I talk a lot and really fast.

fact 5.

My Dad is an author, and my Mum works from home making stuff and selling it online.

DAD
Writes books

MUM
Makes stuff

Chapter 1

I wanted to tell you about the time I learnt all about **ANGELS.**

But get ready!!!

If you're not wearing socks,

put them on,

BECAUSE THIS WILL BLOW YOUR SOCKS OFF!

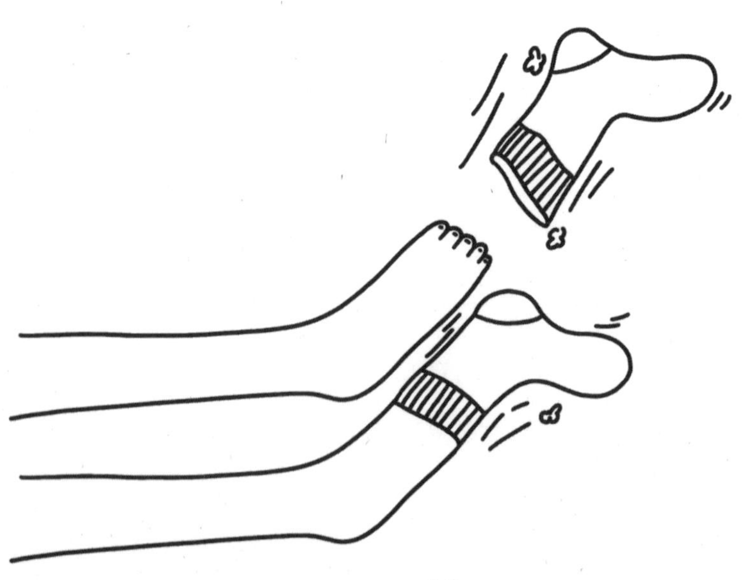

And if you're not wearing any, what if your toenails are blown off instead?!

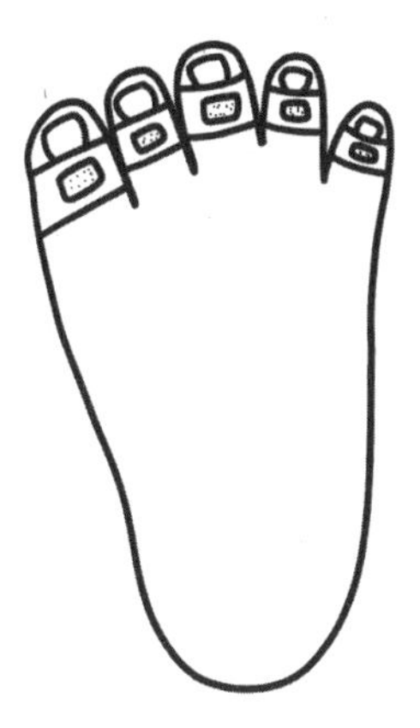

Missing toenails would be very painful.

Safety First.

All set?

Right, so one Friday night, I couldn't sleep. It might have been because of all the cola I drank at my cousin's birthday dinner that evening.

Mum did have her eye on me and had said, "Oi, Eliyas. Just one glass. I am watching you."

But I still managed to pour

without her even noticing, because she was too busy chatting with my aunty. My sister, Aasiya said,

"I'm going to tell MUMMMMMM!"

But she agreed not to
when I gave her one of my cupcakes.
and promised not to do it again.

So that night, I was tossing and
turning over in my bed,
hoping that that would
help. **BUT IT DIDN'T.** So
I decided to go downstairs to eat some
COOKIES, because my best friend
Yahya once told me that cookies are
the answer to everything.

I sat at the kitchen table, with a
plate of Mum's homemade
slighty-not-sweet-enough chocolate
chip cookies,

hoping not to be caught by Mum or Dad. I had only had two, when I heard footsteps coming towards the kitchen ... and I thought,

Chapter 2

The door opened slowly and I held my breath...

It was DAD...

He walked in, sleepily. I didn't even know he was still up, working on one of his books.

"What are you doing up?" he said.

"Can't sleep." I said.

I thought he would send me **straight up to bed**, but instead, he poured me a glass of milk and said,

"You can't have cookies without milk!"

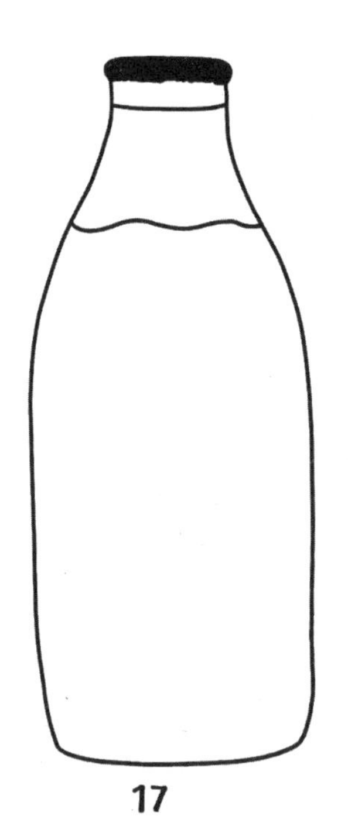

WHAT A DAD! YAY!

He poured himself some too, and before I knew it, I was talking to him about space.

I said, "It must be boring up there, all quiet and lonely, with nobody around." I was trying to be smart. I thought if I said that, Dad would tell me cool stories about **ALIENS**,

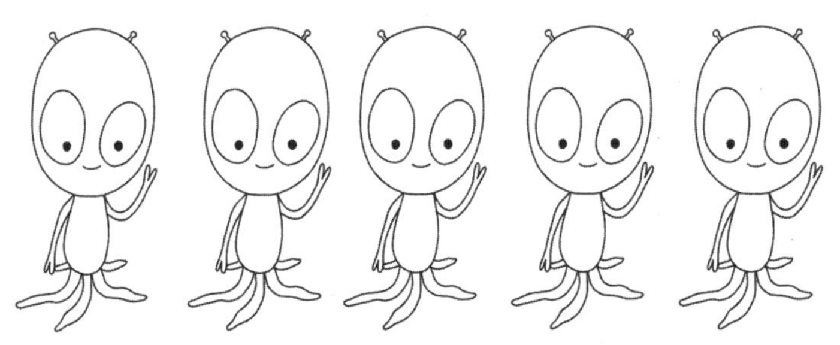

and **ALIEN SPACESHIPS**

and stuff.

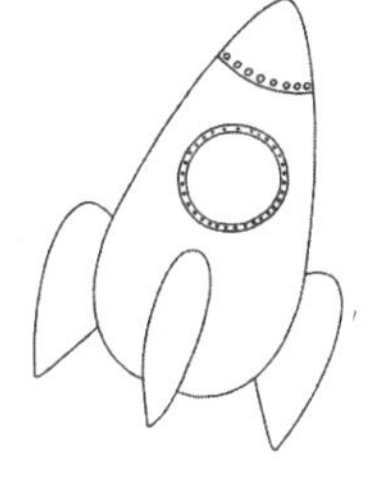

But he said, "Space isn't empty, because it's absolutely

FULL OF angels."

And he spent the next few minutes trying to explain just how many angels there are up there. There are A LOT! Like I mean there are

He told me there are SO MANY ANGELS IN OUTER SPACE that there's not

ONE BIT

of it where there isn't an angel. And because all of them are saying things to praise Allah, the whole of space sounds like it's

I'm not just making that up you know, because NASA (the space scientists) got a recording from up there. Dad knows, because he has a friend that works there.

This is him.

Super smart brain in here.
Pencil for writing down secret space stuff.

I guess it's kind of like when you go to the masjid on EID, and there's nowhere to step, because each space has a human in it. That's what outer space is like – each space has an angel in it. Except maybe the angels didn't have to take their shoes off in a big messy pile of footwear at the door. That's because angels don't wear shoes.

Are you bursting to know more? I was...

ChaPteR 3

"What exactly *ARE* angels?" I asked Dad.

Dad said angels are amazing!

ALLAH MADE THEM FROM LIGHT.

Just like He made us from clay. But they are not like us, they can only do good things, they can't do bad things like humans can, if they want to. They do exactly what Allah tells them to.

I asked him if that means they are

boring and all exactly the same

and he said they

definitely are not!

He said they do have characters and they like some stuff and don't like other stuff so much. And then he said something that totally took me by surprise.

He said, "Is it BORING
to Have
600 wings?"

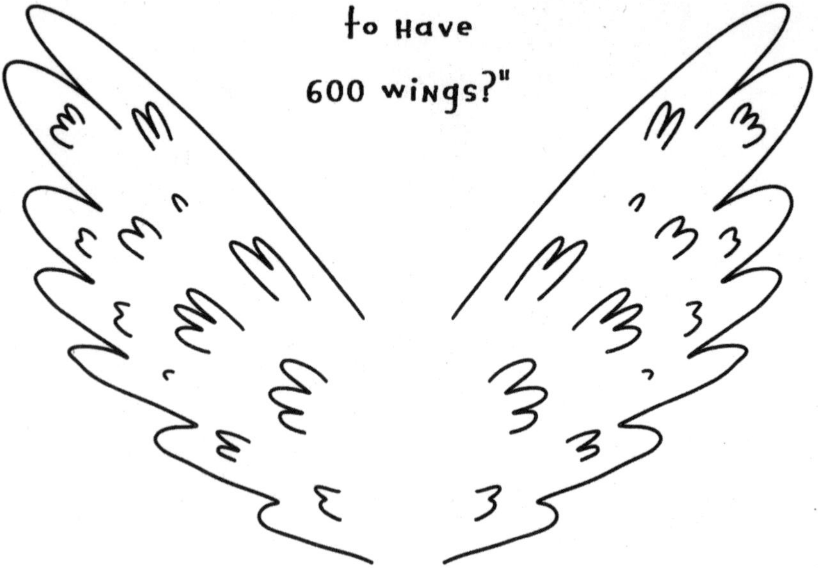

WOAH!
WHAAAAT?
600 WINGS?

I've seen pictures of angels on Google,

and they do have wings, **but not 600!** My dad told me that those Google pictures aren't what angels ACTUALLY look like. He said that when the Prophet (saw) saw

JIBREEL (AS)

he said that he was so **BIG** that he was filling up the space all the way from the ground

to the sky

and that he has six hundred wings. He's a very special angel!

But angels come in different sizes. Some have two wings, and some have more, but they all have wings. Dad said they are **beautiful** and **STRONG.**

"How strong?" I asked, "What's the heaviest thing they can lift? I wonder if they are stronger than Uncle Sam. I wonder if they would feel it if an elephant sat on them. I love elephants. Can they lift an aeroplane?"

My dad burst out laughing, spluttering milk and cookies all over his jumper.

EWWWWWWWWW!

"What's so funny?" I said.
He said, "A plane is nothing. Lifting a plane for some angels, is like lifting an ant for me.

ANGEL JIBREEL (as) can knock over a whole city with the tip of one of his wings. Angels can crush mountains.

WOAHZERS!

Just then, it had started to pour down with rain and my dad said, "Do you know who

ALLAH chose to do that?"

"Who?!"

"An angel called

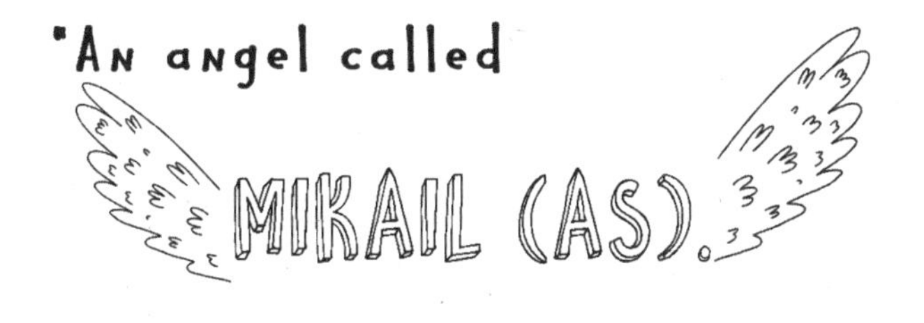

He moves the winds and rains, controls the seasons, and lots more, when ALLAH tells him to."

And there are two angels, with every person, on their shoulders. Writing down the good and bad stuff that the person does and says. And two more angels with every person just to protect them. I did not know that! Did you? I'll tell you more about that later.

And there's lots more that I didn't know...

Chapter 4

I didn't know that angels do not eat, like we do. They don't need food.

I used to think maybe they eat light-bulbs or STARS or something, since they are made of light.

I thought they needed to keep the light going, but no, they just keep going anyway.

Dad said they also don't sleep.

They don't even get tired. And they never get **bored.** Those are things only humans suffer from. And maybe animals. I wonder if animals get bored?

Anyway, all the angels have different **JOBS** to do and they LOVE doing them.

Now, you might be wondering where everyone else was during this awesome conversation between me and Dad. The answer is, that they were

SNNNNOOOORRRRRING

away in their beds. I am not kidding, I could hear Yusuf snoring the whole time. 😝
He snores

SUPER LOUD.

LIKE THERE IS SOMETHING WRONG WITH HIS NOSE.

I was really enjoying having Dad all to myself FOR ONCE, and having a proper chat. But then, as if he sensed that we were having fun without him, Yusuf strolled in so casually and so wide-eyed that anyone would think it was 12 noon, not 12 midnight.

So I basically got annoyed and threw a slightly-not-sweet-enough chocolate chip cookie at him.

But it completely missed, even though I am a **super good shot**. It hit the wall instead and crumbled into a **BIG FAT** COOKIE MESS.

Then dad gave me a look that said,

I'm-not-happy-with-your-disgusting-behaviour

and put Yusuf on his lap.

Then, funnily, he actually laughed and told me that the cookie missing Yusuf, probably had something to do with . . . .

ANGELS

. . . . too, because each person has two angels for PROTECTION in front of us and behind us. And they only get out of the way if Allah has said that something should happen to us. So in this case, maybe, just maybe, an angel whacked that cookie out of the way!

Chapter 5

It was a **SUPER COOL** feeling to know that angels were all around us, protecting us! But apparently, only if we're doing things that Allah likes.

Which makes sense if you think about it (like I did).

because if there was a bad guy, off to do bad stuff, like a burglary, I seriously doubt angels would be protecting him on his way.

It reminded me of the time I was annoyed with Aasiya's room, because Mum and Dad gave it a makeover and she got to have silly girly wallpaper with unicorns ALL OVER IT.

I am Sick of unicorns.

She has them on everything! Her clothes, pencils, toys, books. **EVERYTHING!**

And when she vomited on my bed, because of eating too much candyfloss,

IT WAS THE LAST STRAW.

So I went to get some paint, and was on my way up the stairs with a mind to 'accidently,' squirt some of the blue stuff on her wallpaper,

when my big toe got stuck in my pyjama pants and tripped me up.

As you might have guessed, I fell right on top of the blue paint bottle, which squirted all over the beige carpet instead.

I guess the angels weren't stopping me from tripping up in that moment. And the worst thing about it is that I DIDN'T EVEN GET PUNISHED by Mum and Dad, because they said it was an accident. I still feel guilty every time I go up the stairs and see the light blue stain left over from Dad's scrubbing.

I looked at the cookie crumble mess and felt relieved that I hadn't been a bad shot when throwing it at Yusuf.

He was just being PROTECTED. But finding out that angels are around us just gave me so many more questions in my head!

So I asked Dad, and what he told me, made me FREEZE and also forget that I was dipping a cookie in my milk, which made it go all soggy and drop into the glass.

ARGGGGGGHHHHH I HATE IT WHEN THAT HAPPENS!

But guess what? It was worth it, because what Dad told me next blew my mind!

Chapter 6

I had asked Dad that if angels had protected Yusuf from my cookie, then why didn't I **see** them?

Dad said, "Oh. Haven't you figured that out yet? **Humans can't see them.**"

He said that if we could see them, we would never be able to close our mouths because of what they look like. Our jaws would be dropped all the time, because, basically, they're too amazing.

And then he said that when we pray,

WOAH! WOAH! WOAH!

"Say Subhan-Allah," said Dad.

So I did.

"But HOW can they FIT in my Room?" I asked.

"Well angels aren't like things that have to squash into places. They are made of LIGHT, so they are completely different. ALLAH knows how they fit, or if perhaps some of them is **OUTSIDE** the house. But we know they are there!" Dad grinned, happily.

I got ready to **JUMP** out of my seat so I could go and pray, to be next to angels as BIG as houses. But just then, I did one of the biggest

I have ever heard in my whole entire life.

It was colossal!

Yusuf started laughing.

Now, normally, I would have laughed too, but all I could think about was that

the angels might have run away from me, just like Aasiya does when I burp next to her!

I held my mouth, just in case there were more burps coming. Then I moved my fingers away slowly, just to ask Dad if there was anything that makes angels run away from us.

He said, "GARLIC. AND BAD BREATH."

UH OH!

I'M NEVER GOING TO FIB ABOUT BRUSHING MY TEETH, AND FLOSSING, AND GARGLING, EVER AGAIN! I WILL DO IT TILL MY MOUTH SHINES AND SMELLS LIKE THE BEST MINTY FRESH BREATH THE ANGELS HAVE EVER SMELT!

(Because let's face it, sometimes I am lazy so I just pretend to brush my teeth).

And guess what?! Dad said that if I want to smell nice for the angels, I should always do good things, because when someone starts thinking about doing a good deed, a beautiful scent starts coming from them, which ANGELS love, and come near to!

OH WOW!

I BOUNCED out of my chair and gave Yusuf a hug and a cookie.

"Is that a good deed, Dad?"

"Yes!"

"What else can I do? What else is a good deed?" I BOUNCED about,

excitedly, all over the place.

My body was springy, ready to jump into action for another good deed. Then suddenly, I **banged** into the cabinet behind me, sending all of Mum's pretty teacups crashing to the ground...

Chapter 7

Have you ever heard the sound of

12 teacups BREAKING on a stone floor?

IT'S LOUD.
VERY LOUD.

So loud, that just a few seconds later, Mum and Aasiya came down the stairs, rubbing their eyes.

"What on earth is going on down here?" said Mum.

"Cookies," said Yusuf. Completely ignoring the fact that I had just broken all of Mum's teacups.

Hahahah

Mum didn't find it funny. 

Dad was already clearing up.

"Sorry Mum. I just got too excited because we were talking about angels! I was looking for a good deed to do, but then this happened," I explained, with my shoulders drooping.

Mum didn't know what to say. I guess she couldn't really tell me off for TRYING to do a good deed. So she smiled instead. The kind of smile she smiles when, secretly, she is mad inside.

"Angels?!

I want to hear about angels!" said Aasiya.

"Me too," said Mum, grabbing a cookie.

So Dad carried on.

He said that although we can't see angels, sometimes they come in human shape. When they do that, humans can see them. Like when the angel Jibreel (as) used to come to the Prophet (saw).

When angels come in human shape, they come looking like what the people in the place that they go to, look like.

"Angel Jibreel is the one who goes to all the prophets, isn't he, Dad?" said Aasiya.

She was trying to act angelic and clever, because she had just learnt that at madrassa.

Daid said, "Yes sweetheart, Jibreel (as) is the most IMPORTANT ANGEL.

He was the first living, breathing creature of Allah

and **Adam (as)** was the **first man.**

Allah speaks to the four most special angels, Himself. Sometimes He might speak to angels Mikail or Israfil through Jibreel,

but He ALWAYS speaks to

Jibreel (as)

Himself."

Mum already forgot all about her teacups and joined in excitedly.

"Jibreel (as) is the angel that came down to speak to all the prophets, passing on messages from Allah. He is the one that came to Ibrahim (as) when the people were about to throw him in the fire.

He was the one that came to Hajar (as) when she was searching for water, running from

Mount Safa to Mount Marwa."

"I know that story!" I said, "It's when baby Ismail was crying."

(look who's clever now, Aasiya).

"Yes, absolutely. His mother was HAJAR (AS) and his father was IBRAHIM (AS)."

She carried on and told us that Jibreel (as) HIT the ground, and loads and loads of water came

Hajar (as) carved a well, which isn't a very huge well, but just from that one smack on that ground with his

STRENGTH,

Zamzam water has been flowing out for thousands of years at

8000 LITRES

Per Second,

BY ALLAH'S

COMMAND.

THAT'S VERY FAST!

My mouth was munching and my eyes and ears were wide open, swallowing up all this awesome stuff about angels.

"Angel Jibreel sounds amazing...!" I said, in a daze.

"He is!" said Dad. "And guess what? When **Allah loves someone**, he calls Angel Jibreel and says, 'I love (the person's name), so love that person too."

OH MY ALLAH!

Even though we were all sent off to bed after that, I couldn't sleep. I kept wondering...

Wondering if Allah had ever told Angel Jibreel to love me.

Wondering if an angel was in the room with me.

Wondering if I had ever seen an angel in a human shape, without even knowing it.

Wondering if I had bad breath.

Wondering, wondering, wondering!

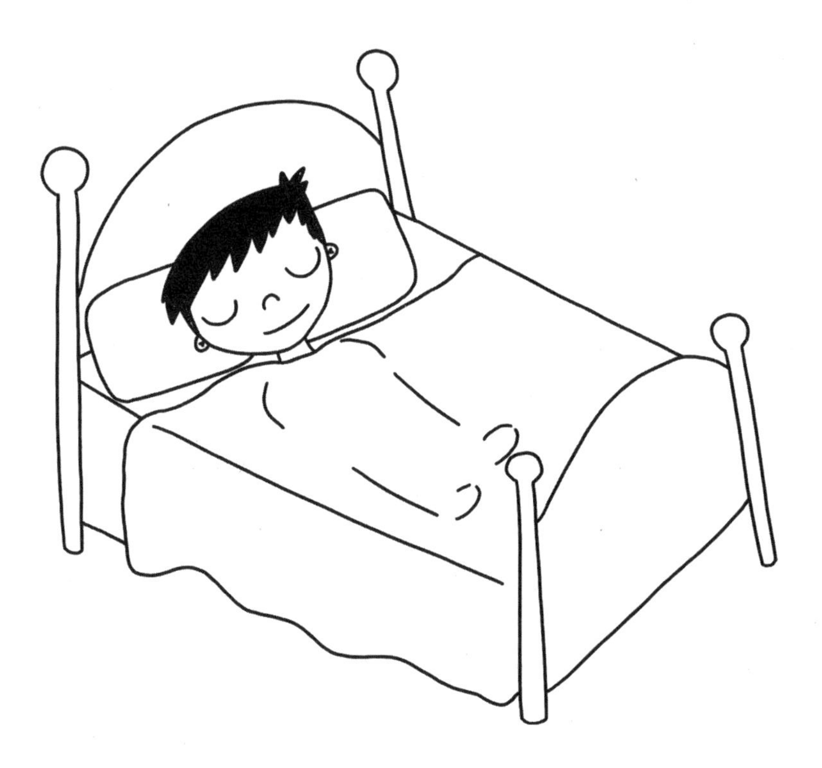

Other cool things angels do

1

When you step out of your door to go out, and say this dua:

BISMILLAHI
TAWWAKALTU
ALALLAHI LA HAWLA
WALA QUWWATA
ILLA BILLAH

The two angels that protect you respond to you.

When you say the Bismillah – in the name of Allah – part of the dua, they say, "In the name of Allah, you've been GUIDED."

When you say, "Tawwakaltu alallah – I put my full trust in Allah," they say, "You've been DEFENDED (against anyone that's going to try to harm you today)."

When you say, "La hawla wala quwwata illa billah – there is no power or might except that belongs to Allah," they say, "And you've been PROTECTED (from all harm of the day)."

And the shayateen* that come to mess with you while you're out and about start getting all hopeless as

*This is the plural of Shaytan

their plans completely **FLOP!** They ask each other, "What can we do with someone who has been GUIDED, DEFENDED AND PROTECTED?!"

OH YEAAAAAH!

TAKE THAT!

YOU CAN'T DO ANYTHING!

So obviously those shayateen run away.

HOW COOL IS THAT?

I think once you know this, it's **absolutely nuts** to ever step out of your house without saying this dua. I made sure I memorised it STRAIGHT AWAY, and now when I go out, I feel INCREDIBLE, like Allah's shield is all around me.

(You can read the hadith from Tirmidhi about this in Zanib Mian's 30 Hadith for Kids book)

2

Remember those angels I mentioned that are on your right and left shoulder that write down all the **good** and **bad** things you do?

Well one cool thing about them is that if you do something bad, Allah tells the angel on the left not to write it down yet. So the angel has to WAIT. And if you are **sorry** for doing that bad thing and say sorry to Allah (do istighfar) then the bad thing you did is never written down and a good deed is written down instead!

YAY!

3

Angels have shifts. Some are with you during the day and others at night. They swap over at Fajr time and Asr time.

At the end of their shifts they report back to Allah about what you did during that time. YIKES! Imagine if you hadn't done ANYTHING nice and the angels were like,

Meh, this person didn't really do anything impressive or kind or worth any rewards.

OR WORSE ...

Imagine if you did something you know Allah wouldn't like!

Have you ever been in a situation where someone had to tell your adults about something really bad you did, and you felt TERRIBLE because you knew they will be upset, well just think about how you would feel if you did something bad in the day and weren't sorry for it, so ALLAH got your NAUGHTY REPORT!

So now, I make sure the angels have nice things to say about me when they take my deeds (the things I did) up to Allah. Obviously, I forgot about that for a minute, when I was taking the paint up to Aasiya's room.

PAINT

So there you go, I explained ANGELS to you. I hope you liked it. If you have any more questions about angels, which you will do if you **wonder** a lot, like me, then you can ask your adults. There's obviously lots more to learn about them than I wrote down here for you. Have fun and remember to brush your teeth!

Other Eliyas Explains titles to look forward to:

Sahabas

Hijrah

Miracles

Super girls

Dinosaurs, Aliens and Unicorns

Israa' and Mi'raj

Ramadan

Aqeedah

www.muslimchildrensbooks.co.uk

IF YOU LIKED THIS BOOK, YOU'LL LOVE THESE!

Welcome to Planet Omar! Zanib Mian's laugh-out-loud series, with amazing cartoon-style illustrations from Nasaya Mafaridik. Perfect for fans of Tom Gates and Wimpy Kid.

* Chosen as *THE TIMES* Children's Book of the Week: 'Mian's gentle mixing of humour and Muslim tradition is fresh and necessary' *

AVAILABLE WIDELY AT ALL BOOKSHOPS